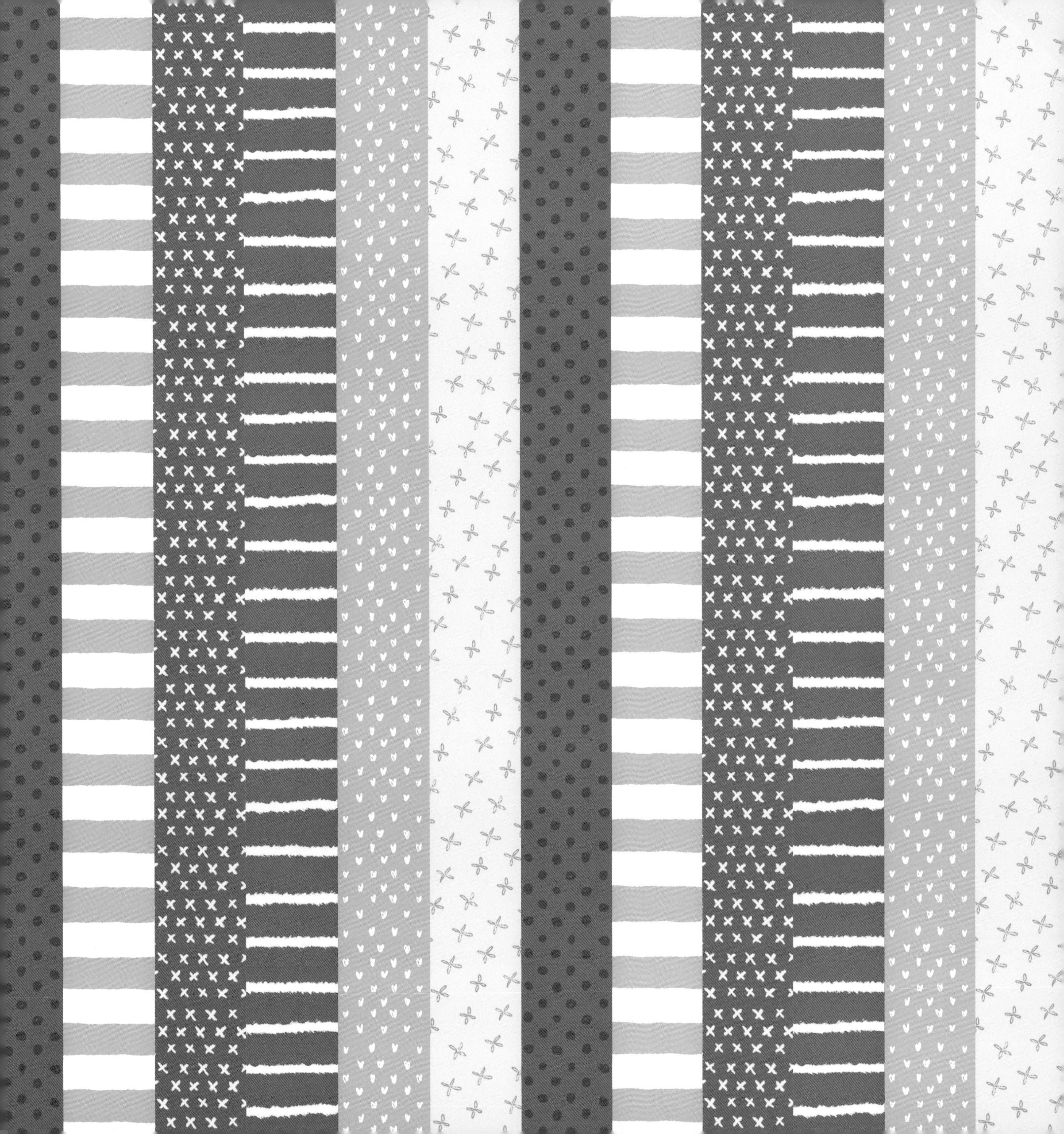

IMAGINE THAT™

Licensed exclusively to Imagine That Publishing Ltd
Tide Mill Way, Woodbridge, Suffolk, IP12 1AP, UK
www.imaginethat.com
Copyright © 2020 Imagine That Group Ltd
All rights reserved
2 4 6 8 9 7 5 3 1
Manufactured in China

Written by Sam Samson
Illustrated by Alex Patrick

ISBN 978-1-78958-481-3

A catalogue record for this book is available from the British Library

GLAMINGO

Written by Sam Samson

Illustrated by Alex Patrick

Flo the flamingo lived by a lake with all of her flamingo friends. But she was different from them in one big way.

Flo loved to dress up!

A little tiara here, a pretty bow there –
she always looked totally fabulous!

All that dressing up made Flo hungry.
Every day, she waded in the water
looking for food.

Flo would eat anything – as long as it was pink. She scooped up yummy pink shrimp, tasty pink plants and anything else she could find.

One day, disaster struck. Flo had eaten so much pink food that there was nothing left.

'Oh no!' said Flo, puffing up her pink feathers. 'No more pink! What will I eat now?'

It was time to be brave and try something new. First, Flo found some blue food and gobbled it up.

But what Flo didn't know was that pink food made her pink. So can you guess what happened next?

As Flo filled her tummy with blue food,
her feathers turned from pink to blue!

'Now I need to change my outfit to match!' said Flo. And off she went to find something new to wear.

Soon, hungry Flo had eaten so much blue food that there was nothing left.

'Oh no!' said Flo, puffing up her blue feathers. 'No more blue! What will I eat now?'

Flo hunted around the lake. She found some green food and gobbled it up – and her feathers turned from blue to green!

'Now I need to change my outfit to match!' said Flo. And off she went to find something new to wear.

But Flo wasn't the only flamingo to change colour.
All her flamingo friends had to find new food
and they changed colour, too.

Before long, the lakeside was filled with an enormous flock of rainbow-coloured flamingos.

'Come on everyone!' Flo called to her friends.
'Let's ALL dress up. Choose something to wear.
It's party time!'

Soon, everyone was dressed in amazing outfits. And they all looked totally fabulous!

As the sun set over the lake, the fabulous, glamorous flamingos danced and danced.

'We're glamingos!' they cried,
and they danced all night.

Many days later, the pink food started to appear in the lake again. And little by little, Flo and her friends turned into pink flamingos once more.

But no one ever forgot the totally fabulous,
rainbow-coloured party.